Usbo

The Wind in the Willows

Retold by Mairi Mackinnon

Illustrated by Olga Demidova

English language consultant: Peter Viney

Contents

3

The Wind in the Willows

32

About the story

33

Activities

38

Word list

You can listen to the story online here:
www.usborneenglishreaders.com/
windinthewilllows

It was a fine spring day, and Mole was working hard in his little house underground. All morning he cleaned walls and washed floors, until finally he said, "Enough!" He put down his cleaning things and ran outside.

He could hear birds singing, and see new spring flowers. "This is better than house-cleaning!" he said. He could see something bright on the far side of the field. The river was shining between tall willow trees, and the trees were moving in the gentle wind. Mole ran towards the water.

He saw a small face on the other side. The Water Rat said, "Hello, Mole! I'm Ratty. Would you like to come over here?"

"How can I do that?" asked Mole.

Ratty stepped into a little boat and rowed across the river, then helped Mole to climb in. "This is exciting," said Mole. "I've never been in a boat before."

"*Never*? Why not?" said Ratty. "It's the most wonderful thing in the world, you know! Listen, if you're not too busy, why don't you come with me? We can take a picnic and stay out all day."

"Oh, yes *please*," said Mole.

Ratty rowed back to his house and fetched the picnic. Then he rowed along the river to a little island. Mole was very hungry, and the picnic was delicious.

At one moment they saw a black and white face on the river bank. "Hello, Badger!" shouted Ratty. "Sorry, Ratty, too many people," said Badger, and disappeared.

"He's always like that," said Ratty. "He's a kind friend, but he prefers being alone. He lives in the Wild Wood. One day we'll go and see him, but we'll have to choose a good time."

They finished the picnic and started rowing back. "Let me try," said Mole.

"Not yet," said Ratty. "It's more difficult than you think." But Mole jumped up, and fell over Ratty, and then the boat turned over and Mole was in the water, going down and down…

Two strong arms pulled him to the bank. "Oh, Ratty, I'm so sorry!" said Mole.

"Don't worry," said Ratty. "You wait here, and I'll bring the boat. And then – would you like to stay with me for some time? I can teach you to swim, and to row, and the river's very nice in the summer."

"Oh, yes *please*!" said Mole.

One morning, Ratty said, "Mole, I'd like you to meet my friend Toad. He talks about himself a lot, but he has a kind heart. You'll like him." They rowed to a beautiful old house by the river.

Toad was sitting outside. "I'm so pleased to see you!" he said. "Come and look at this!"

Behind the house was a little wooden caravan. Toad wanted to show them everything inside. "Isn't it perfect? We're leaving this afternoon."

"Toad, we can't just go," Ratty started to say, but Mole looked sad. "Oh, all right," said Ratty.

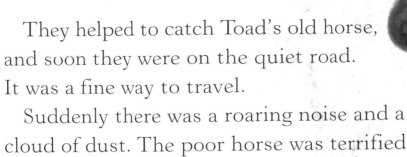

They helped to catch Toad's old horse, and soon they were on the quiet road. It was a fine way to travel.

Suddenly there was a roaring noise and a cloud of dust. The poor horse was terrified, and tried to escape. An enormous car drove past them. As it disappeared, they heard a 'Toot-toot!'

The caravan lay on its side, with a broken wheel. "Oh, Toad, I'm so sorry!" said Mole. "Toad, are you hurt?"

Toad was sitting in the middle of the road and smiling. "Toot-toot!" he said happily. "Toot-toot!"

The months went past, and it was almost winter. Ratty often went to sleep by the fire, and it was much too cold and wet for the boat. "Maybe we can visit Badger?" said Mole, but Ratty never wanted to leave the house.

"I'll just go by myself," Mole decided one afternoon. The sky was pale and the air was cold. Even without their leaves, the tall trees looked beautiful.

In the wood, the trees were closer and
it was much darker. Suddenly Mole saw a
face between the trees – a little, narrow,
unfriendly face. He looked again, and it was
gone – but then he saw another. He heard
the sound of little feet all around him.

Mole was terrified. He started running,
then fell over, then climbed inside a dead
tree. He stayed there in the dark.

Some time later, he heard a strong,
friendly voice. "Mole?"

"Ratty, is that you? Oh, I'm so happy to
see you!"

"Silly Mole, coming to the Wild Wood on your own! We river animals never do that. It's no problem for Badger, of course. He likes it here. He's not afraid of the weasels and foxes – but for us, they're trouble. Let's go home. We can come back another day. Wait a minute – is that snow?"

The snow fell, more and more of it, and it was difficult to see their way through the trees. They walked this way and that, then Ratty stopped and looked around. Were they lost?

Then Mole fell over something. "Oh, my leg! That hurts!"

"Clever Mole!" said Ratty. "Look, it's a doorstep!"

"A doorstep? What a silly place to leave a doorstep," said Mole – but Ratty started digging, and soon they could see a door. "Hello!" Ratty shouted.

They heard a sleepy voice inside. "Who's making that noise, at this time of night?" Then the door opened. "Ratty!" said Badger. "What are you doing here? Are you lost in the snow? Come inside, quickly."

The two animals followed him to a warm kitchen with a wonderful bright fire. Badger took their coats and boots and brought dry clothes. Then he put a hot meal on the kitchen table, and the animals ate until they were full.

"Now, tell me the news about Toad," said Badger.

"Oh, it's bad," said Ratty. "He's a terrible driver, but nobody can tell him that. He crashes his car, then buys a new one, again and again. He's crashed six already. Soon, someone is going to get hurt."

"We must do something," said Badger.
"When the weather is warmer, we'll talk to
him and make him understand. Now, you
need to sleep. Come this way." He showed
them a comfortable bedroom.

In the morning they all had a good
breakfast, and Badger took them back to the
river bank. Soon they were safely at home in
Ratty's little house.

It was spring again when Badger came to Ratty's house. "It's time to visit Toad," he said. "I hear he's bought a new car – another one. We must stop him!"

When the animals arrived at Toad's house, the car was waiting. Toad was on the doorstep. "This is perfect!" he said. "You must come... with..." He stopped when he saw Badger's face.

"Take him inside," Badger told Ratty and Mole. Then he told the car driver, "Mr. Toad has changed his mind. You can take that horrible machine away, thank you."

Inside the house, he said, "Toad, we need to talk." He and Toad went into a quiet room. Ratty and Mole sat outside. They could hear Badger's angry voice. When they heard Toad, he sounded quiet and sad.

Finally the door opened. "Tell them, Toad," said Badger. "Tell them you're sorry, and you'll never drive a car again."

"But I'm *not* sorry," said Toad with a smile, "and I *will* drive again. It's so much fun! I'll show you. The first car I see – toot-toot!"

"Then we'll stay here until you change your mind," said Badger. "You'll stay in your room, and one of us will be with you all the time. You'll be quite comfortable, but you won't leave the house. It's the only way."

Toad looked sad, but he didn't argue. He stayed in his room for a week. One morning, Badger and Mole went out, and Ratty was alone with Toad.

"It's a lovely day," Ratty said.

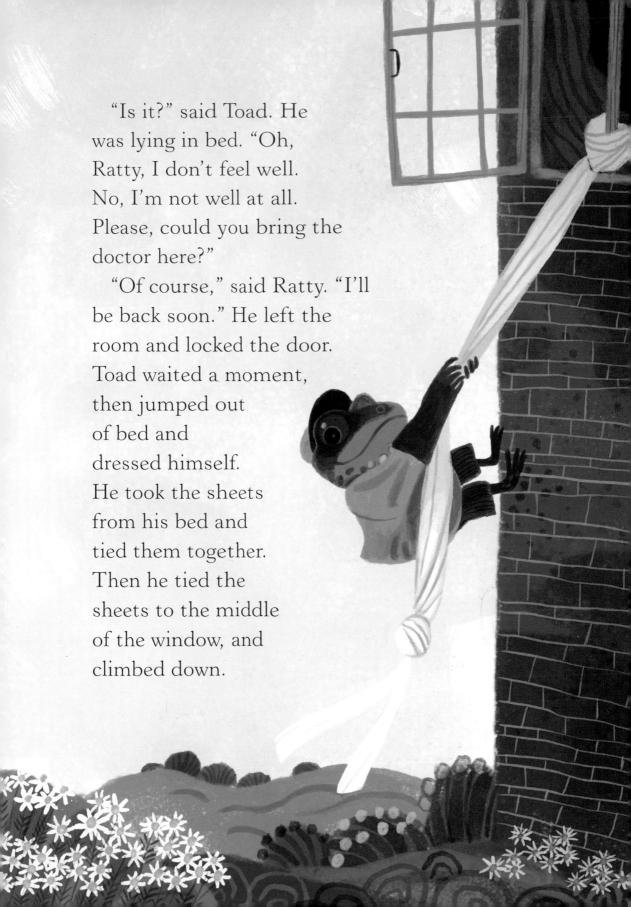

"Is it?" said Toad. He
was lying in bed. "Oh,
Ratty, I don't feel well.
No, I'm not well at all.
Please, could you bring the
doctor here?"

"Of course," said Ratty. "I'll
be back soon." He left the
room and locked the door.
Toad waited a moment,
then jumped out
of bed and
dressed himself.
He took the sheets
from his bed and
tied them together.
Then he tied the
sheets to the middle
of the window, and
climbed down.

"Clever Toad!" he said to himself. He started walking across the fields, and soon he came to a village. In the middle of the main street he saw something wonderful.

"A car!" said Toad. "A lovely, shining blue car!" He walked all around it. "I wonder if it starts easily?"

He turned the starting handle, and there was a roar. Then he was sitting in the car, and the car was moving, faster and faster... Then there was a crash, and Toad was flying through the air.

"You stole a valuable car," said the judge. "You drove very dangerously, and crashed the car, but that's not the worst thing. The worst thing is that you were rude to a policeman."

"I was telling the truth!" said Toad. "He *was* very fat, and very stupid."

"Stop!" said the judge. "Don't argue with me. For stealing the car, I'm sending you to prison for one year. For dangerous driving, three years; but for being rude to a policeman, fifteen years. That's nineteen years, so let's say twenty. Now take him away!"

and again, but it didn't help him. The police took him and dressed him in prison clothes. Then they threw him into a dark prison room, and locked the door. Toad lay on the floor and cried some more. "Twenty years! When will I see my friends again?"

For two weeks he lay there and cried, and he didn't want to eat. "You poor thing," said a friendly voice. "It's not fair." It was the prison guard's daughter. She was a kind girl, and she felt sorry for Toad.

She started to bring his meals, and she talked to him about his home and his friends. "He's not a bad animal," she thought. "He shouldn't be here."

One day, she said, "Toad, do you know my aunt? She washes the prisoners' clothes. She takes them out on Mondays, and brings them back clean on Fridays. I was thinking, you look rather like her..."

"I do not!" said Toad.

"Listen to me, you silly thing. Tomorrow is Friday. I'll speak to my aunt. You can change clothes with her, and then you can escape."

"Ha ha, yes!" said Toad. "I like it! I'll do it!"

The next evening, a small person in a
pink dress and hat left the prison. "Good
night! Goodbye!" it said to the guards.

Away from the prison, Toad started
dancing. "Clever, clever Toad! The strongest
prison in England can't hold me! But it's a
long way home, and I'll have to walk. Maybe
I should find somewhere to rest first."

There was a small wood next to the road.
Toad soon found some dry leaves, and made
a bed and went to sleep.

In the morning, the sunlight woke him.
He could see light on water, and he hurried
towards it. There was a canal, and Toad
could see a horse on the path beside it. The
horse was pulling a narrow canal boat.

"Good morning," said the boatwoman.
"Are you enjoying your walk?"

"Not really," said Toad. "I'm tired, and the
path is dusty, and my feet hurt."

"Where are you going?" asked the boatwoman. Toad told her. "Well, that's lucky! I'm going that way too," said the boatwoman. "Jump on the boat. What work do you do?"

"I wash clothes," said Toad. "I'm famous for it."

"That's even better!" said the boatwoman. "I have all these sheets to wash, but I never have time. Wait, I'll get you some soap and water."

"It can't be so difficult," thought Toad, but half an hour later he was hot and tired, the soap was gone and the sheets were as dirty as before.

"What a mess! You've never washed clothes in your life!" laughed the boatwoman.

"Of course not!" said Toad. "A Toad does not wash clothes. A Toad drives fast cars, and escapes from prisons, and –"

"A horrible Toad! On my boat!" screamed the boatwoman. She picked Toad up and threw him in the water.

He swam to the bank and sat there. "What am I going to do now?" he wondered.

"Can I help you? *Toad*? Is it really you?" Toad knew that voice. "Ratty! Oh, it's good to see you."

"Toad, what are you wearing? Come and find some dry clothes."

Soon Toad was at Ratty's house, and he was dry and dressed. "Now it's time to go home!" he said. He stood up.

"Oh, Toad, I'm very sorry," said Mole, "but the Wild Wood weasels are in your house and we can't go near it.

Toad was so angry that he couldn't speak. "Don't worry," said Mole. "Badger has a plan."

Badger arrived that afternoon. "There are weasels and foxes everywhere," he said, "but tomorrow, there'll be a big party for old Grandfather Weasel's birthday. Now, Toad, many years ago your father told me about a secret passage. It goes all the way from the river bank to the middle of your home, so I was thinking..."

"Yes!" said Toad. "We'll surprise them!"

They spent all the next day planning and getting ready. When it was dark, Badger took them to the secret passage and they followed him inside.

When they came up into the house,
they could hear loud singing. "This way!"
shouted Badger. He opened the door and
they all ran through.

The weasels stopped singing. They seemed
to see angry Badgers and Moles and Rats
and Toads everywhere. All those terrible
animals were shouting and running towards
them with big, heavy sticks.

The weasels ran this way and that way, between tables and through doors and out of windows, until the four friends were alone in the room.

"Oh, Toad, what a mess," said Ratty sadly.

"Don't worry, we can clean the place tomorrow," said Mole. "And then, Toad, *you* must have a party."

Toad held out his arms. "You are the best friends in the world, and I am a very lucky Toad. Thank you all. It's good to be home."

About the story

Kenneth Grahame was born in Scotland in 1859. When he was five, his mother died and he went to live with his grandmother in the country near the River Thames. He had many happy memories of this time, and was probably thinking about his childhood when he wrote about Mole and Ratty on the river.

As an adult, Grahame worked for the Bank of England, but he also wrote stories for magazines. He began to write a story for his son, Alastair, about the animals of the river bank. Some people think that Toad in *The Wind in the Willows* was rather like Alastair in real life. *The Wind in the Willows* became a book in 1908, and millions of children and adults have read and loved it ever since.

Activities

The answers are on page 40.

Four friends

Pick *one* sentence for each animal.

Mole...   Ratty...   Toad...   Badger...

A.
...isn't afraid of
weasels and foxes.

B.
...likes to have lots of
people around him.

C.
...is a
terrible rider.

D.
...is very rude to
a policeman.

E.
...doesn't want to leave
the house in winter.

F.
...doesn't really like
picnics.

G.
...wants to learn how to
row and swim.

H.
...is good at
washing clothes.

Mixed-up story

Can you put these pictures and sentences in order?

A.

"A lovely, shining blue car!"

B.

Badger just said, "Too many people," and disappeared.

C.

"Tell them you're sorry, and you'll never drive a car again."

D.

"I'll just go by myself," Mole decided.

E.

"I've never been in a boat before."

F.

One morning, Ratty was alone with Toad.

G.

He put down his cleaning things and ran outside.

H.

"Now, tell me the news about Toad," said Badger.

I.

"Silly Mole, coming to the Wild Wood on your own."

Clever Toad

One word is wrong. Can you find it and
choose the right word instead?

1.

Toad was sitting in the middle
of the wood and smiling.

road　night　room

2.

Toad stopped when he saw
Badger's wife.

home　shoes　face

3.

"I was telling the judge!"
said Toad.

horse　truth　time

4.

"It can't be so dirty,"
thought Toad.

lucky　difficult　late

Say why

Choose the right ending for each sentence.

1.

Mole fell in the river because...

A. ...he didn't know how to row.

B. ...Ratty pushed him.

2.

Toad stayed in his room for
a week because...

A. ...he was very tired.

B. ...Badger told him to.

3.

The boatwoman threw Toad in
the water because...

A. ...he was very rude to her.

B. ...she didn't like toads.

4.

Toad couldn't go back to
Toad Hall because...

A. ...there was too much snow.

B. ...there were weasels and
foxes everywhere.

Weasel party

Which three things *can't* you see in the picture?

cake   chair   door   fork

moon   plant   spoon   stick

table   tail   water   window

Word list

argue (v) when you don't agree with someone and you say so, sometimes quite angrily, you argue.

aunt (n) your father's sister or your mother's sister.

badger (n) a wild animal, about the size of a cat. Badgers have black and white faces and live under the ground.

bank (n) the land beside a river.

canal (n) a canal is a man-made river. Canals help people to travel from one place to another by boat.

caravan (n) a caravan is like a little house on wheels, pulled by a horse or a car.

change your mind (v) when you are going to do something, then you decide to do something different, you change your mind.

crash (v) to hit something very suddenly and hard, often by accident.

doorstep (n) a long, flat piece of stone or concrete outside the door of a house.

dust (n) a very light, fine powder. There is often dust on dry roads and paths, or inside old buildings.

fox (n) a wild animal like a dog, with red-brown fur and a thick tail.

guard (n) someone who protects a person or a place.

handle (n) something that you use to hold, carry or open something, or to make something work, with your hand.

judge (n) when a person has broken the law, a judge decides whether they need to pay money or go to prison.

lock (v) you lock a door or a box with a key so that nobody else can open it.

mess (n) when a place is not clean and tidy, it is a mess.

mole (n) an animal with dark fur, about the size of a mouse. Moles live under the ground and are good at digging.

narrow (adj) the opposite of wide.

passage (n) a narrow way between rooms or between parts of a building.

picnic (n) an informal meal that you eat out of doors.

prison (n) a place where criminals have to stay, sometimes for years, as a punishment for their crimes.

roaring (adj) like the noise a wild animal makes when it is angry.

row (v) to move a boat forward in the water using long wooden paddles called oars.

rude (adj) the opposite of polite.

sheet (n) a thin cotton cover on a bed. You sleep on a sheet, sometimes with another sheet and more covers over you.

silly (adj) foolish, not sensible.

soap (n) you use soap with water to wash yourself, or to wash plates, clothes and other things.

stick (n) a piece of wood from a tree.

terrified (adj) badly frightened.

toad (n) a small animal like a frog. Toads usually have rougher skin than frogs.

water rat (n) a European animal that lives beside rivers and streams. Water rats have smaller, rounder faces and bodies than ordinary rats.

weasel (n) a small wild animal with a long, red-brown body and tail. Weasels hunt other, smaller animals.

willow (n) a tree that often grows near water. 'Weeping' willows have long leaves and branches that hang down.

Answers

Four friends
Mole - G
Ratty - E
Toad - D
Badger - A

Mixed-up story
G, E, B, D, I,
H, C, F, A

Clever Toad
1. ~~wood~~ road
2. ~~wife~~ face
3. ~~judge~~ truth
4. ~~dirty~~ difficult

Say why
1. A
2. B
3. B
4. B

Weasel party
moon, plant, water

You can find information about
other Usborne English Readers here:
www.usborneenglishreaders.com

Designed by Laura Nelson Norris
Edited by Jane Chisholm
With thanks to Laura Cowan
Digital imaging: Nick Wakeford

Page 32: portrait of Kenneth Grahame © Lebrecht Authors/Bridgeman Images.

First published in 2019 by Usborne Publishing Ltd.,
Usborne House, 83-85 Saffron Hill, London EC1N 8RT, England.
www.usborne.com Copyright © 2019 Usborne Publishing Ltd.